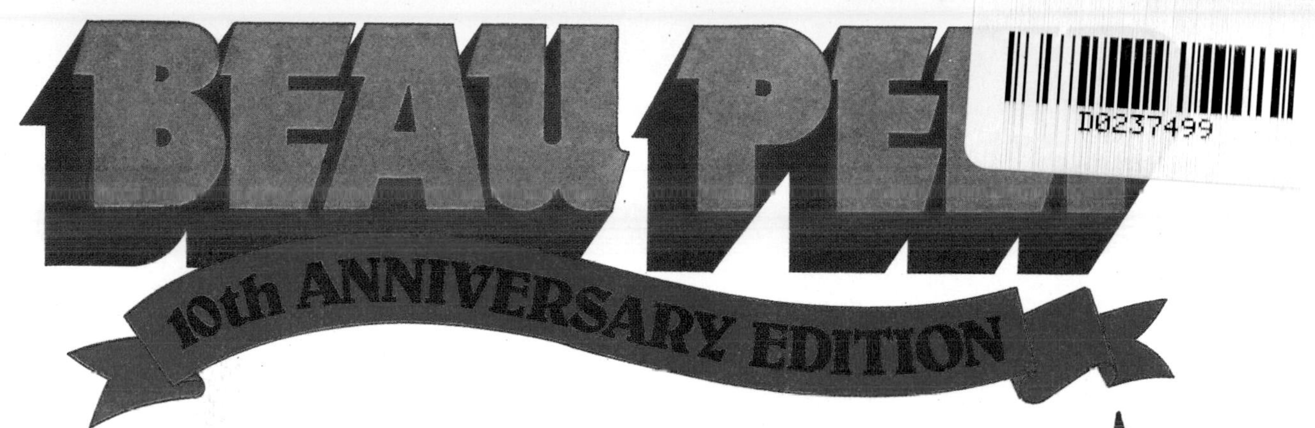

From The

DAILY STAR

245 Blackfriars Road,
London, SE1 9UX.
Printed by Grosvenor Press
(Portsmouth) Ltd.,
Reproduction by
Graphic Origination, London.
Co-ordinated by
Roeder Print Services Ltd.,
London.

ISBN 0-85079-190-1

WELCOME.

£2.

BEAU PEEP

EGON

THE NOMAD

MAD PIERRE

DENNIS

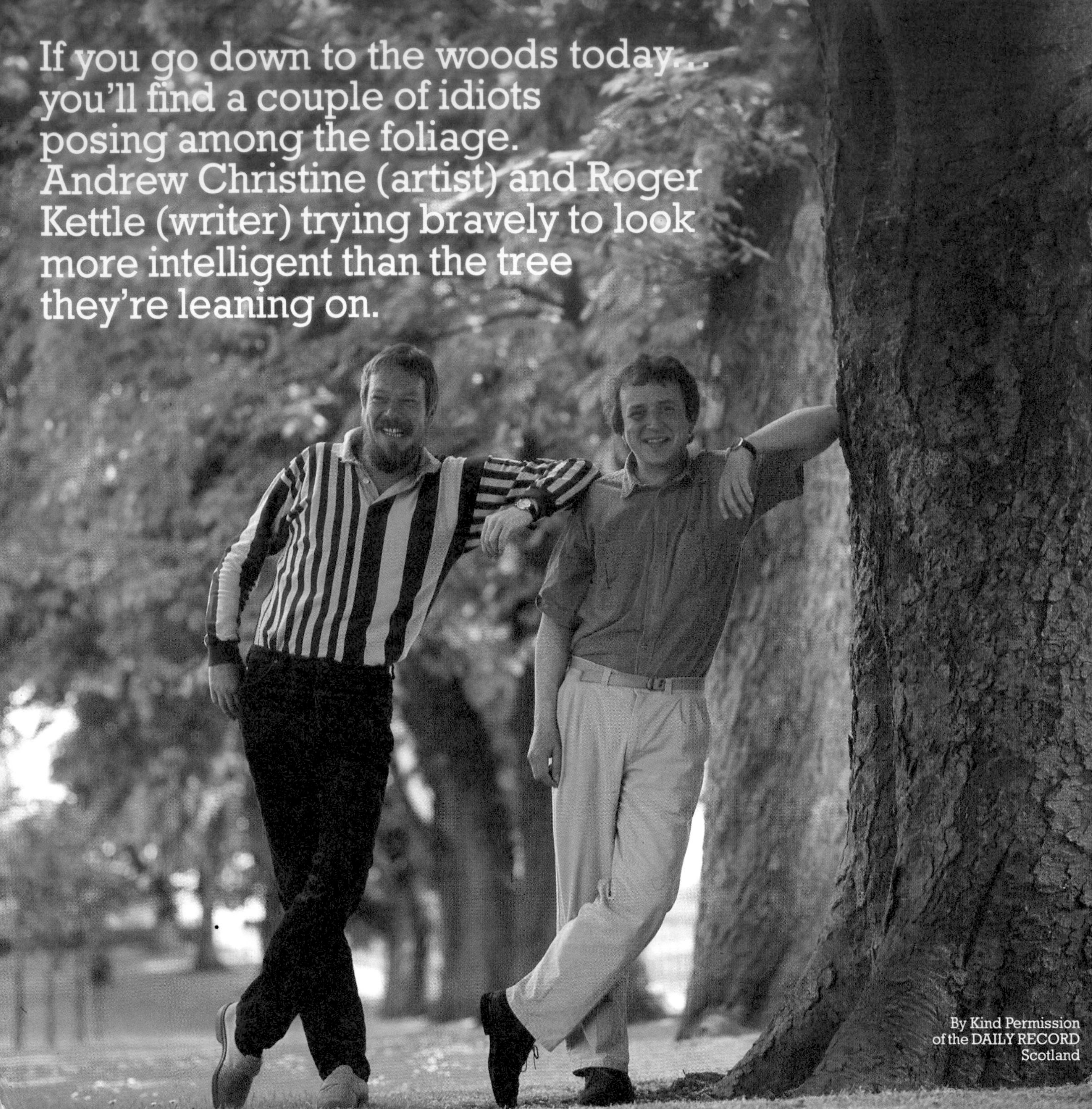
If you go down to the woods today...
you'll find a couple of idiots
posing among the foliage.
Andrew Christine (artist) and Roger
Kettle (writer) trying bravely to look
more intelligent than the tree
they're leaning on.
By Kind Permission
of the DAILY RECORD
Scotland

THE ADVENTURES OF LEGIONNAIRE BEAU PEEP

FROM THE DAILY STAR

YOU MUST DELIVER THIS LETTER TO FORT AL-BERNAAD.

IT'S TOP SECRET AND IT MUST GET THROUGH.

DO YOU HAVE ANY QUESTIONS?

WHAT'S THE POSTCODE?
2232

WELL, THAT'S PEEP ON HIS WAY.

IT'S VITAL THAT HE GETS THAT LETTER THROUGH— ALL OUR LIVES DEPEND ON IT.

2233
COULD YOU OPEN THE GATE, SARGE? I MUST HAVE LEFT THE LETTER ON MY BUNK.

THIS LETTER MUST BE REALLY IMPORTANT.

THE SARGE SAYS I'VE TO DIE RATHER THAN LET THE ENEMY HAVE IT.

2234
HALT!
I'VE GOT A LETTER FOR YOU.

NEVER BEFORE HAVE I SEEN SUCH A COWARD...

...A MAN WHO SURRENDERS WITHOUT A FIGHT. A MAN WHO OFFERS MONEY FOR HIS LIFE...

2235
AND A CHEQUE— I'LL POST THAT WHEN I GET BACK.

NOW I HAVE AN IMPORTANT DECISION...

...SHOULD I WASTE A BULLET ON A COWARD LIKE YOU?

FUNNILY ENOUGH, I WAS SHOPPING YESTERDAY AND I COULDN'T BELIEVE THE PRICE OF THEM!
2236

I BOUGHT THIS QUIZ BOOK TO HELP PASS THE TIME.
2237

WE CAN ANSWER QUESTIONS ON OUR STRONGEST SUBJECT.

I'LL SEE IF THERE'S ANY ON BLOWING BUBBLES.

RIGHT, DENNIS—WHAT SUBJECT DO YOU WANT TO ANSWER QUESTIONS ON?
MUSIC!
QUIZ BOOK
2238

MUSIC? YOU DON'T KNOW ANYTHING ABOUT MUSIC!
I DO, TOO!

GO ON—ASK ME WHAT A PIANO IS!

ASK ME QUESTIONS ON SPORT, BEAU.
OKAY.
2239

"NAME THE TYPE OF SLEDGE USED IN THE WINTER OLYMPICS."
I KNOW THIS!

I DO! I KNOW THIS!
GO ON, THEN.

A TOBACCO!
CLICK!

I NEVER GET ANY QUESTIONS RIGHT.
2240

NOT ONE. I'VE NEVER EVEN GOT ONE.

I'LL NEVER GET ONE, EITHER.
WHERE IS PEKING?

SEE? IT COULD BE IN CHINA FOR ALL I KNOW.

PEKING IS IN CHINA?
YES.
2241

YOU MEAN I GOT A QUIZ QUESTION RIGHT?
YES.

I DID IT! I GOT A QUESTION RIGHT!

WHAT IS A PEKING ANYWAY?

IT'S A PROMISE— I WON'T CALL YOU STUPID EVER AGAIN.
2252

I WANT YOU TO HAVE MY LAST TOFFEE AS A GIFT.

REMEMBER, DON'T EAT THE WHITE, CRINKLY STUFF ON THE OUTSIDE.

BEAU...
2242

...AND I DON'T WANT ANY OF YOUR MORONIC REMARKS ABOUT ART.

YOUR INFANTILE OPINIONS ARE OF NO INTEREST TO ME!

I JUST WANTED TO SAY YOUR FLY WAS OPEN.

WHAT A BEAUTIFUL SCENE!

JUST LOOK AT THE SUBTLETY OF COLOUR ON THESE DUNES...

...AND HOW THE SUNLIGHT CREATES A THOUSAND TONES.

I THINK I'LL DO THEM ORANGE!
SLAP! SLAP!
2243

LET ME WORK THIS OUT.
THE SUNLIGHT IS COMING FROM OVER MY RIGHT SHOULDER...

...THEREFORE THE DARKEST TONES OF SHADE WILL BE TO THE LEFT.
IT'S HELL TRYING TO KEEP BEER COOL OUT HERE.
2244

THIS IS DEFINITELY MY FINEST WORK YET!

I'VE CAPTURED THE SAND TEXTURE PERFECTLY...

...AND THAT LIGHT! THE WARMTH OF THAT PURPLISH TWILIGHT GLOW...

...REFLECTING FROM HER G STRING!
2245

I'M GOING TO GIVE THE COLONEL MY LATEST PAINTING.
COLONEL ESCARGOT

HE'S A MAN OF BREEDING AND CULTURE.

HE CAN APPRECIATE A STUDY OF THE FEMALE NUDE WITHOUT SNIGGERING.

STONE ME YOU DON'T GET MANY OF THESE IN A POUND!
2246

I'VE JUST READ YOUR REPORT.

YOU SAY YOU WERE AMBUSHED BY ABOUT 54 OF THE ENEMY.

NO, NO! IT SAYS HE WAS ABOUT 5'4."
2258

OH, NO—
MAD PIERRE'S JUST COME IN!
2247

I'LL PRETEND I'VE DROPPED SOMETHING AND MAYBE HE WON'T SEE ME.

TWO GLASSES OF WINE, PLEASE

PIERRE WANTS ME TO BUY HIM ANOTHER DRINK.
2248

I'LL PRETEND I HAVEN'T NOTICED HIS GLASS IS EMPTY.

SNAP!

DIFFICULT.
CRUNCH! CRUNCH!

BUY ME MORE DRINK.

WHY DO *I* HAVE TO KEEP PUTTING MY HAND IN MY POCKET?

'COS OTHERWISE I'LL TEAR IT OFF AND PUT IT IN MINE.

LET'S HAVE SOME SERVICE HERE!
2249

I CAN'T BUY YOU ANY MORE DRINKS, PIERRE.

I'M BROKE— YOU'VE SPENT ALL MY MONEY.

BE REASONABLE— WHAT MORE CAN I DO?

HOW MANY DRINKS CAN I GET FOR THESE CLOTHES?
2250

HERE I AM ABOUT TO PAWN MY CLOTHES TO BUY ***YOU*** A DRINK!

WHY DO I LET YOU HUMILIATE ME LIKE THIS?

'COS IF YOU DON'T, I'LL PULL YOUR LUNGS OUT.

THAT'S IT— I COULDN'T REMEMBER FOR A SECOND!
CLICK!
2251

WHAT ON EARTH IS THIS?
2264

I'M EXPERIMENTING WITH A NEW STYLE OF COOKING.

YOU'VE HEARD OF THE CHINESE STIR-FRY METHOD?
YES.

THIS IS STIR-TOASTING.

IF ONLY I COULD GET INTO THAT FORT.

THE MAIN PROBLEM IS THAT THE WALLS ARE 40FT. HIGH...

...AND MY INSIDE LEG'S 2FT 4".
2253

SOMETIMES YOU GET GOOD IDEAS...

...SOMETIMES YOU GET BAD ONES...
BOING!

...AND THEN THERE ARE OTHER TIMES...

...WHEN YOU'RE A KICK IN THE PANTS OFF GENIUS!
BOING!
2254

I'VE GOT THAT FEELING AGAIN.

THAT FEELING SOMETHING STRANGE IS GOING TO HAPPEN.
BOING!

OH, DON'T BE SILLY, BEAU!

IT'S PROBABLY JUST YOUR IMAGINATION!
DAMN!
2255

ALL I NEED IS ONE GOOD BOUNCE...
BOING!

...THEN I'LL BE ABLE TO DECAPITATE THE SENTRY!
BOING!

SWISH!

DAMN! BE BACK IN A SECOND — I FORGOT MY SWORD.
2256

HA-HA! JUST ONE MORE BOUNCE ON MY TRAMPOLINE!
BOING!

KICK IT AWAY, NOW, DENNIS!

SPLAT!

I JUST WANT YOU TO KNOW I HATE YOU.
2257

ACHMED HAS NOTICED A NICK ON THAT TREE.
2270

HE'LL BE ABLE TO RECOGNISE THE MEANING OF IT.

IT'S PROBABLY SOME SORT OF TRIBAL WARNING REGARDING ENEMY MOVEMENTS.

I'VE GROWN AN INCH SINCE LAST YEAR!

LOOK OVER THERE, DENNIS.

TWO VERY ATTRACTIVE WOMEN SITTING ALONE.
2259

I WONDER IF WE SHOULD SUGGEST JOINING THEM FOR COCKTAILS.

HEY, DARLINGS, FANCY GETTING DRUNK AS RATS?

THOSE TWO WOMEN LOOK PRETTY CLASSY.

THEY PROBABLY DON'T MIX WITH THE LIKES OF US.

I KNOW! LET'S PRETEND WE'RE IN OIL!
RIGHT!
CLICK!

GLUB! GLUB! GLUB! GLUB!
2260

COOEE! HELLO, GIRLS!
DENNIS, STOP IT.

WOMEN LIKE THAT NEED A BIT OF RESPECT.

THEY'RE CULTURED... DIGNIFIED.

NOTE THE RAISED PINKIES AS THEY PASS THE SPITTOON.
2261

WHAT ARE YOU DOING, BEAU?

I'M WRITING A NOTE TO THOSE WOMEN...

... A SORT OF FORMAL INTRODUCTION AND A REQUEST TO JOIN THEM FOR COCKTAILS.
2262

ASK IF THEY WANT TO PLAY POSTMAN'S KNOCK!

IT'S A REPLY FROM THOSE TWO WOMEN WE SENT THE NOTE TO.

THEY HAVE A SUGGESTION FOR US!
2263

GREAT! WHERE WILL I PUT THIS BOTTLE?

I'M COMING TO THAT BIT.

WHY DO I ALWAYS GET THINGS WRONG, DENNIS?

MAYBE IT'S BECAUSE YOU'RE UGLY.

YOU'RE A WONDERFUL COMFORT TO ME, DENNIS.
2275

BEAU, WOULD YOU WRITE A LETTER FOR ME?

LET ME SEE– YOU WRITE TWO LETTERS A YEAR...

...ONE TO YOUR MOTHER ON HER BIRTHDAY AND THAT'S PAST...

...SO I PRESUME IT'S THE EARLY "DEAR SANTA I WANT A BIKE."
2265

RIGHT, DENNIS– FIRE AWAY.

"DEAR SANTA, TWO QUESTIONS FOR YOU."

"CAN I HAVE A BIKE?"

"OR DO YOU WANT A FACE-FULL OF KNUCKLES?"
2266

"DEAR SANTA"

"I'VE DECIDED NOT TO ASK YOU FOR A BIKE."

"IT SEEMS PRETTY SILLY AT MY AGE."

"WHY NOT SEND BEAU THE MONEY AND HE'LL BUY IT FOR ME?"
2267

WELL, THERE'S YOUR LETTER TO SANTA ALL DONE.
GREAT!

NOW I'M GOING TO SIT AND WISH AND WISH AND WISH!

HE'S JUST LIKE AN INNOCENT LITTLE KID!

THO' IT'S A PITY I COULDN'T FIND SOMETHING TO BLACKMAIL HIM WITH.
2268

I SUPPOSE YOU HAVE TO BE REALLY CLEVER TO WORK FOR SANTA.

OH, EXTREMELY. THERE'S A LOT OF ORGANISING TO DO.

DO YOU THINK I COULD EVER BE A SHELF?
THAT'S "ELF," DENNIS. I DOUBT IT.
2269

AHA!

JUST AS I THOUGHT!
WHAT IS IT?
2276

I'VE LOST MY BINOCULARS.

A MAGAZINE, EH? GIVE, US A LOOK!

DENNIS, I REALISE YOU ASSOCIATE THE WORD "MAGAZINE" WITH NAKED WOMEN...
2277

...BUT IT MAY SURPRISE YOU TO KNOW THAT NOT ALL OF THEM CONTAIN SUCH PHOTOGRAPHS.

THIS ONE DOES, THOUGH—LOOK AT HER!

LET'S DO THIS DAFT MAGAZINE QUIZ.

"HOW DO YOU RATE AS A CASANOVA?"
WHAT, LIKE STEW?

THAT'S A CASSEROLE, DENNIS.
2278

THIS QUIZ WILL SHOW HOW ROMANTIC YOU ARE.
2279

"YOU ARE WALKING YOUR GIRLFRIEND HOME AND—"
HANG ON.

IS IT DARK?
I SUPPOSE SO.

THEN SHE'S WALKING ME HOME.

HERE'S THE NEXT QUESTION, DENNIS.
2280

"IT'S YOUR GIRLFRIEND'S BIRTHDAY. DO YOU BUY HER (A) DINNER? (B) CHOCOLATES? (C) FLOWERS?"

THAT'S A DIFFICULT ONE...

I USUALLY DUMP THEM BEFORE THEIR BIRTHDAY.

"HOW ROMANTIC ARE YOU?"— QUESTION 10.
2281

"DO YOU NOTICE WHEN YOUR GIRLFRIEND GETS A NEW DRESS?"

I DID LAST TIME...

...THE POLICE MADE HER TAKE IT BACK.

YOU'VE GOT THE LOWEST SCORE POSSIBLE.
2282

AS A ROMANTIC YOU RATE ZERO.
ME?

TAKE YOUR ANSWER FOR "HAVE YOU EVER BLOWN GENTLY IN A GIRL'S EAR?"

"ONLY TO GET THE WAX OUT."

THIS ISN'T JUST A ROBE—IT'S MY HERITAGE.
HONEST ABDUL
2283

MY FAMILY HAVE WORN GARMENTS LIKE THIS FOR CENTURIES.

IT'S A SYMBOL OF OUR PEOPLE TO BE WORN WITH PRIDE AND DIGNITY...

...BUT, OKAY—I'LL DO IT FOR A QUID.
HONEST ABDUL'S AUTUMN SALE

THIS COULD BE MY BIG BREAK!
HONEST ABDUL'S AUTUMN SALE

THERE'S A LOT OF MONEY IN ADVERTISING THESE DAYS.
HONEST ABDUL'S AUTUMN SALE

OF COURSE, ANY CAMPAIGN I TOOK ON WOULD HAVE TO BE RESTRAINED AND TASTEFUL.

MAYBE I COULD DRESS UP AS A GIANT HAMBURGER!
2284

'MORNING!
2285

SHORTLY, I SHALL RETURN THAT GREETING.

I MAY EVEN GO ON TO DISCUSS ANY INTERESTING EVENTS OF YOUR DAY...

...BUT FIRST, A WORD FROM OUR SPONSOR.
HONEST ABDUL'S AUTUMN SALE

I DON'T BELIEVE THIS!
HONEST ABDUL'S AUTUMN SALE
2286

HAVE YOU SUNK SO LOW THAT, LITERALLY, THE CLOTHES ON YOUR BACK ARE FOR SALE?

AND MY SHORTS!
OCT. 16TH OCT. 20TH

JUST LOOK AT YOU — YOU'VE SOLD YOUR PRIDE AND DIGNITY!
HONEST ABDUL'S AUTUMN SALE

YOU REALLY BELIEVE THAT?
YES, I DO.

THAT'S RIDICULOUS! I WOULD NEVER DO THAT!

UNLESS, OF COURSE, YOU WANT TO BUY THEM.
2287

MY FATHER USED TO SAY "LIFE IS LIKE A PAIR OF TROUSERS..."
2288

"...EXCEPT FOR THE LEGS AND THE POCKETS."

I SHARE MY BLOOD WITH A LOONIE.

NOT AGAIN, DENNIS— THOSE PET SHOP PEOPLE ARE CROOKS!
PET SHOP

I BOUGHT A BABY KANGAROO — YOU SHOULD SEE IT JUMP!
PET SHOP
2289

IT'S A FROG, DENNIS.
RIBBET!
PET SHOP

ARE YOU SURE IT'S NOT A KANGAROO!
PET SHOP

DENNIS, IT'S A FROG. KANGAROOS ARE BIG AND HAIRY WITH POUCHES.
PET SHOP
2290

THAT THING DOESN'T EVEN HAVE A HANDBAG.
PET SHOP

BELIEVE ME, DENNIS—THAT IS NOT A KANGAROO.
WHAT YOU HAVE THERE IS GREEN, THREE INCHES LONG AND SAYS "RIBBET."
PET SHOP
2291

IT ALSO LAYS MILLIONS OF EGGS WHICH BECOME—
GOT IT!
CLICK!
PET SHOP

IT'S A HEN!

DENNIS, IT IS NOT A KANGAROO AND IT IS NOT A HEN!
PET SHOP

JUST LISTEN TO IT!
RIBBET!
PET SHOP

RIBBET! RIBBET!
PET SHOP

IT'S A RABBIT!
RIBBET!
PET SHOP

I'VE CALLED MY PET FROG "WEBBY."
PET SHOP

THAT'S QUITE CLEVER, DENNIS—I DIDN'T THINK YOU'D NOTICE ITS FEET.
PET SHOP

PET SHOP

IT DOESN'T SPIN WEBS, THEN?
PET SHOP

HAVE YOU STILL GOT YOUR PET FROG?
YEP.

I PUT HIM IN MY BACK POCKET TO... TO...

COULD I BORROW A FISH SLICE AND A SPONGE?

ARE YOU COMING TO THE PUB TONIGHT?
NO, THANKS...

...I WANT TO FINISH THAT NEW BOOK I BOUGHT.

YOU FOUND YOUR CRAYONS, THEN?
2559

IT'S FASCINATING WATCHING YOU COLOUR IN YOUR BOOK.

I CAN TELL WHICH CRAYON YOU'RE USING JUST BY LOOKING AT YOUR FACE.
HOW?

RED—TONGUE TO THE RIGHT. BLUE—TONGUE TO THE LEFT.
2560

I SUPPOSE A COLOURING BOOK CAN BE QUITE THERAPEUTIC.
2561

PSYCHOLOGICALLY SPEAKING, IT MAY WELL REMOVE TENSION, SOOTHE ANXIETY AND CREATE AN AWARENESS OF ARTISTIC VALUES.

WHAT COLOUR'S A PIG?

YOU SHOULDN'T BE SO LITERAL WITH YOUR COLOURING-IN, DENNIS.
2562

THE SKY ISN'T JUST BLUE, YOU KNOW.

IT CAN BE A MILLION SHADES OF A MILLION DIFFERENT COLOURS!

YOU'VE COLOURED IN MY BEST GLASSES, DENNIS.

STOP TELLING ME HOW TO COLOUR IN MY BOOK!
2563

YOU'RE JUST JEALOUS 'COS YOU'VE NOT GOT ONE!
ME?

YOU WOULDN'T CATCH ME DOING ANYTHING AS CHILDISH AS THAT!

AND IF I DID, I WOULDN'T GO OVER THE LINES LIKE YOU DO!

IT'S BOUND TO HAPPEN OF COURSE...

...BATTLE-HUNGRY FIGHTERS, STARVED OF ACTION ALL COOPED UP TOGETHER.
2564

WHAT HAPPENED?
HE TORE MY BOOK!
HE TRIED TO STICK A CRAYON UP MY NOSE!

WHAT ARE YOU DOING, BEAU?
2565

I'M ENTERING A COMPETITION — I HAVE TO ANSWER 5 QUESTIONS.

COO! CAN I HELP?

YES — YOU CAN LICK THE STAMP.

WHAT DO YOU HAVE TO DO IN THIS COMPETITION?
2566

I HAVE TO IDENTIFY 5 CITIES FROM CLUES.

THE FIRST ONE'S EASY — IT'S GOT A LEANING TOWER!

I'M DOING THIS, DENNIS, TO STOP THE WORD "BLACKPOOL" COMING OUT.

CLUE Nº2 — "A CITY FAMOUS FOR ITS CANALS."

THAT'S EASY — RIGHT HERE!
WHAT?

WE'VE GOT CANALS WITH TWO HUMPS AND WE'VE GOT CA—

HERE'S A POUND, DENNIS — GO AND SEE IF THE BRAIN-CELL SHOP IS STILL OPEN.
2567

WHAT DO YOU GET IF YOU WIN THIS COMPETITION?

A LUXURY HOLIDAY FOR TWO.
TWO?

I SUPPOSE YOU'LL WANT TO TAKE YOUR BEST CHUM?
OF COURSE.

BUT WE'LL SEND YOU A CARD.
2568

LET'S SEE—I'VE GOT TO COMPLETE THE FOLLOWING SENTENCE.
2569

"I LIKE CHOCKY-WOCKY BARS BECAUSE..." AND I'VE GOT TO USE 12 WORDS.

NO, YOU CAN'T HELP, DENNIS.

YOU ONLY KNOW 8 AND 5 ARE FILTHY.

DID YOU POST MY COMPETITION ENTRY?
YES.
2570

IT HAD TO GO THIS MORNING OR IT WOULD BE TOO LATE.
I KNOW!

I'M NOT STUPID! I CAN POST A LETTER!

I TORE THE STAMP OFF FIRST — I COLLECT THEM.

YOU STAY HERE, PEEP, AND WATCH FOR THE ENEMY.
2571

DO YOU KNOW HOW TO SIGNAL WITH A MIRROR?

COOEEE!

THIS LOOK-OUT JOB IS A CINCH!
2572

I MIGHT AS WELL GET COMFY AND HAVE 40 WINKS.

MY SUPER-SHARP HEARING WILL PICK UP A FOOTSTEP HALF A MILE AWAY!

YOU WANT ME TO INFORM ON MY COMRADES?
2573

HA! YOU CAN TORTURE ME FOR DAYS IF YOU LIKE...

...BUT YOU'D ONLY BE WASTING YOUR TIME!

I FLAKE OUT AFTER TEN SECONDS.

WHERE ARE THE REST OF YOUR MEN?
2574

CONSIDER MY MOUTH FIRMLY ZIPPED.

PERHAPS I SHOULD SHOOT YOU?

SUDDENLY MY FLIES ARE OPEN!

YOU'RE GOING TO LEAVE ME TO BAKE IN THE DESERT SUN?
2575

WITHOUT FOOD, WITHOUT WATER, WITHOUT ANYTHING?

PERHAPS I AM BEING A BIT HARSH

THANKS A MILLION.

IT'S PEEP! THE ENEMY HAVE BURIED HIM UP TO HIS NECK IN THE SAND!

SERGEANT! THANK GOODNESS YOU'VE COME!
2576

COULD YOU TURN THE PAGE FOR ME?

YET ANOTHER STROKE OF GENIUS!
FIRST, I BRUSH AN OLD SHEET WITH GLUE...
...SECOND, I COVER IT WITH SAND...
...AND THIRD—HEY PRESTO! I BECOME A REMARKABLY LIFELIKE SAND-DUNE!
GLUE
2577

I MUST SURELY BE THE WORLD'S GREATEST LIVING DISGUISE EXPERT!
2578

I DEFY ANYONE TO GUESS THAT I'M NOT REALLY A SAND-DUNE!

WHAT'S THAT?
IT'S THE NOMAD UNDER A SHEET THAT'S HAD SAND GLUED ON IT.

GOOD MORNING, NOMAD.
I'M STUNNED! HOW DID YOU KNOW I WASN'T A SAND-DUNE?
2579

WELL, GENERALLY SPEAKING, THE PATTERNS ON A DUNE FORM RIPPLES, WHICH CURVE AWAY FROM THE PREVAILING WIND.
AND THEY TEND NOT TO WEAR SANDALS.

I REALLY THOUGHT MY SAND-DUNE DISGUISE WOULD FOOL YOU.
2580

APART FROM THE SANDALS, WOULD YOU HAVE KNOWN IT WAS ME?
YES...

...A SAND-DUNE IS SIX TIMES MORE INTELLIGENT.

YOU HAVE INSULTED MY HONOUR!
2581

BUT YOU DON'T HAVE ANY HONOUR!

I HATE IT WHEN PEOPLE HAVE YOU OVER A BARREL.

I'LL HAVE YOUR HEAD ONE DAY, BEAU PEEP!
2582

WHEN I BECOME KING OF THE WORLD, YOU'LL BE FIRST AGAINST THE WALL!

BY THE WAY, HAVE YOU VOTED?
VOTE NOMAD FOR KING OF THE WORLD.

POLITICS IS DEFINITELY THE LIFE FOR ME!
VOTE NOMAD
KING OF THE WORLD

I THRIVE ON THE INTELLECTUAL CUT AND THRUST OF IT ALL!
VOTE NOMAD
KING OF THE WORLD

BRING OUT YOUR BABIES! BABIES KISSED WHILE YOU WAIT!
VOTE NOMAD
KING OF THE WORLD
2583

A VOTE FOR ME IS A VOTE FOR HONESTY, INTEGRITY AND DECENCY!
VOTE NOMAD
KING OF THE WORLD

VOTE NOMAD
KING OF THE WORLD

AND IT'S WORTH A POUND TO YOU!
VOTE NOMAD
KING OF THE WORLD
2584

FIRST OF ALL, FRIENDS, I WILL ABOLISH TAX!
VOTE NOMAD
KING OF THE WORLD

IN FACT, I WILL INSIST THAT THE TAX OFFICE GIVES EACH OF YOU A MILLION POUNDS A YEAR!
VOTE NOMAD
KING OF THE WORLD

NO POINT PIDDLING ABOUT WITH 2p OFF BEER!
VOTE NOMAD
KING OF THE WORLD
2585

I DON'T SEEM TO BE DOING TOO WELL.
VOTE NOMAD KING OF THE WORLD

I KNOW—WHAT I NEED IS A CATCHY SLOGAN!
VOTE NOMAD KING OF THE WORLD

VOTE NOMAD KING OF THE WORLD

VOTE FOR ME OR I'LL SET DOGS ON YOU!
VOTE NOMAD KING OF THE WORLD
2586

AHA! I SEE YOU'VE ENTERED THE WORLD OF POLITICS!
VOTE NOMAD KING OF THE WORLD

YOU KNOW, I NEARLY WENT INTO THAT BUSINESS MYSELF.
WHY DIDN'T YOU?

OVER-QUALIFIED— I COULD READ AND WRITE.
2587

I'VE DECIDED TO RETIRE FROM POLITICS.
WHY'S THAT?
2588

POLITICS IS A NASTY BUSINESS RIFE WITH BRIBERY AND CORRUPTION.

WELL, I'M DAMNED IF I COULD FIND ANY OF IT!

WHO WOULD YOU MOST LIKE TO HAVE BEEN IN HISTORY, DENNIS?
2589

LET ME THINK... ROBIN HOOD!

GOOD CHOICE! A NOBLE CHAMPION OF THE PEOPLE IN THEIR STRUGGLE AGAINST OPPRESSION!

I'VE ALWAYS WANTED TO WEAR GREEN TIGHTS!

ROBIN HOOD FOUGHT SOMEONE CALLED NORMAN...

...AND THE SHERIFF'S POSSE CHASED HIM INTO SHERBET FOREST.

PROMISE ME, WHEN YOU DIE, YOU'LL LET MEDICAL SCIENCE LOOK AT YOU.
2590

ANYWAY, ROBIN HOOD LIVED IN SHERBET FOREST WITH HIS STAFF...
2591

STAFF?
YES, HE HAD A MAID CALLED MARION, AND-

STOP.

I CAN ONLY TAKE SO MUCH STUPIDITY BEFORE BREAKFAST.

SO YOU THINK YOU KNOW EVERYTHING ABOUT ROBIN HOOD?
YEP!

ALL RIGHT — HOW DID LITTLE JOHN GET HIS NAME?

WHO?
2592

LITTLE JOHN WAS ROBIN HOOD'S FRIEND...
2593

...BUT HE WAS *REALLY* CALLED JOHN LITTLE.

ROBIN REVERSED THE NAME AS A JOKE.

WHAT, HOOD ROBIN?

YOU HAVE SMASHED THE BOUNDARIES OF IGNORANCE, DENNIS.
2594

THERE ARE NO LIMITS TO THE STUPIDITY YOU ARE CAPABLE OF ACHIEVING.

COO, THANKS A LOT, BEAU!

JUST LOOK AT THIS STEW, EGON.!

HAVEN'T YOU EVER HEARD OF PRESENTATION?

FOOD SHOULD APPEAL TO THE EYE AS WELL AS THE STOMACH.

THANK YOU.
2595

WHAT DO YOU MEAN "PRESENTATION"?

WELL, FOOD LOOKS BETTER WITH A BIT OF GARNISH.

YOU COULD DECORATE IT WITH CUCUMBER.

IT'S A GIFT YOU HAVE, EGON, A GIFT.
2596

HOW TO MAKE A TOMATO BUTTERFLY.
GARNISHES

MAKE SLITS IN TOMATO AT 'A' AND 'B'.
CHOP! CHOP! SQUELCH!
GARNISHES

GARNISHES

WHAT'S THAT?
A TOMATO SLUG.
2597

HERE'S A FUN TIP FOR YOUR PARTIES.

TRY MAKING YOUR GUESTS' INITIALS WITH SLIVERS OF CUCUMBER.

MIND YOUR MOUTH ON THE NAILS.

THIS WILL BE A MASTERPIECE OF PRESENTATION!

USING A SCALPEL, I WILL CARVE A RADISH INTO THE SHAPE OF A REARING STALLION!

WHERE'S EGON?
GETTING HIS THUMB SEWED BACK ON.
2599

THIS IS ALL YOUR FAULT—GOING ON ABOUT FOOD PRESENTATION!

I WAS TRYING TO CUT SHAPES FROM A RADISH.
DID THE KNIFE FLIP?

NO, THE AXE.

CLEAN FINGERNAILS— THE MARK OF A GOOD SALESMAN.
HONEST ABDUL
2601

IT'S THAT ATTENTION TO DETAIL WHICH MAKES ME THE TOP TRADER IN THE AREA.

THAT AND A PLENTIFUL LOCAL SUPPLY OF IDIOTS.

DO PEOPLE FAIL TO RESPECT YOU ?
YES.
DUL
2602

DO THEY TREAT YOU LIKE A NOBODY ?
YES.

WHAT YOU NEED IS A SYMBOL OF AUTHORITY, MATURITY...
DUL

WHAT ARE YOU DOING, DENNIS ?

WHAT ON EARTH IS IT ?
A PIPE.
2603

I'VE ALWAYS WANTED TO LOOK MATURE AND SENSIBLE.

AND THIS IS YOUR LAST FLING BEFORE YOU START. ?

DENNIS, THAT PIPE LOOKS REALLY STUPID!
2604

YOU'RE JUST JEALOUS 'COS IT MAKES ME LOOK MORE EXTINGUISHED!

THE ONLY PIPE IN THE WORLD MADE FROM LESS WOOD THAN THE HEAD IT'S STUCK IN.

WOMEN FIND PIPE-SMOKERS ATTRACTIVE.

TRUE, DENNIS, BUT SOME PIPES HAVE MORE CHARM THAN OTHERS.

YOURS, UNFORTUNATELY, HAS AN IDIOT STUCK ON THE END OF IT.
2605

MY TROUBLE WAS I LOOKED TOO YOUNG...
2606

...BUT THIS PIPE MAKES ME MORE GROWN-UP.

I LOOK WISE AND MATURE NOW.
WHY DON'T YOU LIGHT IT?

WHAT, AND MELT THE CHOCOLATE?

THIS SHOULD BE GOOD! I ENJOY A BIT OF MUSIC!
BAR
TONIGHT DISCO

BAR
CLACK! CLACK!
TONIGHT DISCO

BAR

WHERE ARE YOU GOING?
BAR
2607

WHAT DO YOU KNOW ABOUT MUSIC?
ME?
TONIGHT DISCO
2608

I KNOW EVERYTHING ABOUT MUSIC! I'M THE KING OF THE TURNTABLE...

...I'M A FINKY J.D.!
CLICK!
THAT'S "FUNKY" AND IT'S "D.J."

IT'S SPECIAL REQUEST TIME!
TONIGHT DISCO
2609

ANY FAB SOUND YOU WANT! ANY GROOVY, COOL, SLICK BEAT YOU DIG, MAN.

HAVE YOU GOT "THE FARMER'S IN HIS DEN"?

THIS ONE'S FOR ALL YOU COOL CATS OUT THERE IN LONELYLAND...
TONIGHT DISCO

...JUST CLOSE YOUR EYES AND DRIFT WITH THE MUSIC IN THE ARMS OF A SPECIAL LOVED ONE.

HANG ON—THIS IS "TRAIN SOUNDS VOL. II."
2610

DO YOU HAVE ANY CLASSICAL RECORDS?
CLASSICAL?
TONIGHT DISCO
2611

DO US A FAVOUR, GRANDAD, AND LISTEN TO YOUR SQUARE SOUNDS ELSEWHERE!

C'MON KIDS, LET'S BOOGIE ON DOWN TO "HOW MUCH IS THAT DOGGIE IN THE WINDOW"?

OKAY, GUYS AND GALS, IT'S LAST DANCE TIME!
TONIGHT DISCO

SO LET'S TURN ON THE SMOOCHIE CHARM AND SWAY THOSE HIPS!

ARE YOU TAKING YOURS BACK FOR A COFFEE?
2612

WE CAN WIN THIS, DENNIS!
BAR
TONIGHT
SPORTS QUIZ

I'LL TAKE THE QUESTIONS ON FOOTBALL, CRICKET, RACING AND BOXING.
WHERE DOES THAT LEAVE ME?
AT THE BAR, GETTING THE PINTS.
TONIGHT
SPORTS QUIZ
2613

REMEMBER TO CONSULT BEFORE ANSWERING, DENNIS.
SPORTS QUIZ TEAM B
2614

WHO RAN THE FIRST 4 MINUTE MILE?
BOLTON WANDERERS!

SPORTS QUIZ TEAM B

BY THE WAY, WHAT DOES 'CONSULT' MEAN?

WHICH BOXER WAS KNOWN AS "THE BROWN BOMBER"?
SPORTS QUIZ TEAM B
2615

KIRK DOUGLAS!

I HOPE THEY GET HARDER THAN THIS— WE'RE STROLLING IT!

WHERE IS THE GRAND NATIONAL HELD?
AINTREE.
SPORTS QUIZ TEAM B
2616

HANG ON! HANG ON! DON'T COUNT THAT!

IT'S WEMBLEY— WE KNEW ALL THE TIME!

WHAT ARE YOU TRYING TO DO— BLOW THE WHOLE THING?

DENNIS, DO ME A FAVOUR AND THINK BEFORE ANSWERING.
SPORTS QUIZ TEAM B
2617

WHO WON 4 GOLD MEDALS AT THE BERLIN OLYMPICS?
BOBBY CHARLTON!

NO POINT WASTING TIME THINKING WHEN I KNEW THE ANSWER.

TONIGHT SPORTS QUIZ
NOT ONE QUESTION RIGHT!
2618

I'VE HEARD SOME STUPID ANSWERS IN MY TIME BUT YOU TOPPED THE LOT TONIGHT!

YOU'RE NOT STILL GOING ON ABOUT THE ASTON VANILLA ONE!

I'VE BEEN STUDYING YOGA.
2619

IT'S SUPPOSED TO HELP ME CONTROL MY TEMPER.

WHACK!

BUT IT DOESN'T— IT ANNOYS ME.

IT'S EASY TO CONTROL YOUR TEMPER, PIERRE.
2620

IF SOMETHING ANNOYS YOU, COUNT TO TEN.

1...2...3...

IF THERE'S ONE THING THAT MAKES MY BLOOD BOIL, IT'S COUNTING!

PIERRE'S IN A FOUL MOOD TODAY—I'LL TRY TO CHEER HIM UP.
2621

ANYTHING I CAN DO FOR YOU, PIERRE?

YES, BLEED.

OF COURSE! I KNOW HOW TO STOP HIM BEING VIOLENT!
2622

I'LL SING TO HIM — "MUSIC SOOTHES THE SAVAGE BEAST."!

LAH-DE-DAH-DE—
WHACK!

THOUGH IT OBVIOUSLY DOES DAMN ALL FOR THE SAVAGE FIST.

HERE'S A CHALLENGE FOR YOU, FOUREYES.
2623

SAY OR DO SOMETHING THAT DOESN'T MAKE ME WANT TO PUNCH YOU.

WELL DONE! I LOVE WATCHING PEOPLE BEING SICK WITH FEAR!

I WONDER IF I SHOULD MENTION TO PIERRE THAT THERE'S A PIECE OF FLUFF ON HIS JACKET?
2624

WHY NOT? I DON'T SEE HOW THAT COULD POSSIBLY UPSET HIM.

APPARENTLY, HEARING ANY WORD WITH THREE 'F's IN IT DRIVES HIM BERSERK.

BEAU, WOULD YOU READ THIS LETTER FOR ME? IT'S FROM MY MUM.
2625

Dear Dennis, Uncle Albert has left you £20,000.

I LOVE YOU.

WHAT?
IT'S TRUE– YOUR UNCLE ALBERT HAS LEFT YOU 20 GRAND!

YAH-HA! HA-HAR!

HA-HAH! HAR-HA...

WHAT IS A GRAND?
2626

DENNIS, YOUR UNCLE HAS LEFT YOU £20,000.
2627

YOU'RE A VERY RICH MAN!

ENOUGH TO BUY A BIKE?

STILL STUPID BUT VERY RICH!

I'M NOT GOING TO TREAT DENNIS ANY DIFFERENTLY.
2628

THE FACT THAT HE'S INHERITED £20,000 IS NEITHER HERE NOR THERE.

BY THE WAY—LEAVE YOUR UNIFORM OUT TONIGHT AND I'LL LICK THE MUD OFF.

BEING WEALTHY, DENNIS, WILL BRING YOU PROBLEMS.

YOU'LL FIND PEOPLE'S ATTITUDE TOWARDS YOU WILL CHANGE.

THEY'LL TRY ANYTHI— MY GOD, A PEBBLE! WALK ON ME!
2629

ANOTHER LETTER, DENNIS? LET ME READ IT FOR YOU, PAL.

PROBABLY JUST CONFIRMATION OF THE MONEY YOU'VE INHERITED.

Dear Dennis, Hope you liked my April Fool's Joke.

ACCORDING TO MY ESTIMATIONS, DENNIS, YOUR ENTIRE FAMILY HAS THE I.Q. OF A TOOTHBRUSH.
2630

OH, NO—IT'S THAT REPORTER AGAIN...
2631

...THE ONE WHO'S ALWAYS LOOKING FOR SENSATIONAL STORIES.

WELL, HE WON'T FIND ANYTHING TO WRITE ABOUT HERE.

"EXCLUSIVE—THE LEGIONNAIRE WHO TALKS TO HIMSELF!"
PRESS

I'M DOING ANOTHER PIECE ABOUT THE LEGION.
2632

NOTHING SENSATIONAL— JUST THE HARD FACTS ABOUT A TOUGH LIFE.

WELL, THAT'S OKAY—YOU CAN ASK ME YOUR QUESTIONS.
PRESS

BEEN TO ANY NAKED ORGIES?
PRESS

I WON'T TAKE PART IN ANY "SENSATIONAL" STORIES.
OF COURSE NOT.

THIS WILL BE ABOUT ONE MANS DREAM...
PRESS
2633

...HIS DREAM OF VICTORY IN A BATTLE OF SURVIVAL.
PRESS

TALKING ABOUT DREAMS, EVER DREAM ABOUT NAKED LADIES?
PRESS

IT'S NOT EASY BEING A REPORTER.
2634

SOMETIMES PEOPLE JUST REFUSE TO TALK TO YOU.

DO YOU KNOW THE TWO WORDS I DREAD MOST?
"NO COMMENT"?

NO— "LAST ORDERS."

LISTEN, THERE IS NO SCANDAL OR VICE IN THE LEGION!
2635

WE MARCH, WE FIGHT, WE OBEY WE SWEAT!

NAKED?

HAVEN'T YOU HEARD OF FREEDOM OF THE PRESS?
BOOT!

THAT'S IT! I'M FINISHED WITH JOURNALISM—NO MORE REPORTING!

ZOOM!

"TOP REPORTER RUN OVER BY CAMEL!"
2636

MY TYPE OF WARFARE IS OUT-DATED AND OBSOLETE.
2637

IT'S TIME I TOOK ADVANTAGE OF TODAY'S TECHNOLOGY.

HOW DID YOU GET IN?
I HIT THE SENTRY OVER THE HEAD WITH A COMPUTER CATALOGUE.

HERE IS A LIST OF MY DEMANDS, MISERABLE DOG!
2638

WHAT'S VIELLA ICE-CREAM?
THAT'S "VANILLA".

HA! THEY SAID I COULDN'T DO IT!

THEY SAID I COULDN'T TAKE OVER THIS FORT SINGLE-HANDED!

WHACK!

THEY HAD A POINT.
2639

WHAT DID YOU DO WITH THE NOMAD?
HE'S IN JAIL.

WE WANT HIM TO SWEAT FOR A BIT— GET REALLY WORRIED!

WE WANT HIM IN AN ABSOLUTE FRENZY OF DREAD AS TO THE PUNISHMENT AWAITING HIM!

ZZZZZZZZZ
2640

I SUPPOSE YOU'LL TORTURE ME NOW— IS THAT IT?

HANG ME BY THE THUMBS FROM THE WALL?

STAKE ME OUT IN THE BURNING SUN?

100 LINES—"*I MUST BEHAVE IN FORT.*"
2641

BOOT!

HEAR MY WORDS, BEAU PEEP— I SHALL RETURN!

BEWARE MY BLADE WHEN THE COCK HAS CROWED THREE TIMES AND THE MOON IS FULL!

THAT'S THURSDAY— HALF PAST SEVEN FOR EIGHT.
2642

THIS IS A GOD-FORSAKEN PLACE, DENNIS.

A BARREN WASTELAND OF SAND AND ROCKS.

IT'S A BIT LIKE LIVING INSIDE YOUR HEAD.
2643

JUST LOOK AT THIS PLACE, DENNIS.
2644

BAKING HOT BY DAY... FREEZING BY NIGHT... AN EXPANSE OF LIVING HELL.

WHAT BRINGS A MAN HERE?

WELL, I GOT THE BUS.

I'M JUST IMAGINING THAT I'M HOME RIGHT NOW.

I'D BE STROLLING IN A MEADOW, MARVELLING AS A THOUSAND BLOOMS AND BLOSSOMS SCENTED THE AIR.

I'D BE LEGLESS IN "THE DOG AND FERRET."
2645

I WONDER WHAT MY MUM'S DOING NOW?
2646

NO DOUBT, SHE'S SITTING IN HER FAVOURITE CHAIR, KNITTING AWAY.

WHAT D'YOU THINK YOUR'S IS DOING?

18 MONTHS

THE CRICKET SEASON WILL JUST HAVE STARTED AT HOME.

Y'KNOW, I USED TO BE A PRETTY MEAN BOWLER!

ME TOO—I HATED BUYING DRINKS.
2647

YOU KNOW HOW WE'VE BEEN TALKING ABOUT HOME?
YES.
2648

I'M TRYING TO REMEMBER THE WORD FOR IT...

...Y'KNOW, WHEN YOU KEEP TALKING ABOUT THE OLD DAYS...

DRUNK?

HIC! FRIGHTEN ME!
WHAT?

I'VE GOT HICCUPS. DO SOMETHING TO FRIGHTEN ME.
HIC!

THAT'S A TOUGH ONE...

I WISH I HADN'T BURNED THAT PHOTO OF MY DORIS.
HIC!
2649

HIC! GIVE ME A FRIGHT TO GET RID OF THESE HICCUPS.

LET ME THINK– WELL, I GET FRIGHTENED BY THE SIGHT OF BLOOD...
HIC!

WHACK!

NOPE–DOESN'T BOTHER ME! HIC!
2650

I KNOW JUST THE THING TO FRIGHTEN AWAY MAD PIERRE'S HICCUPS!
HIC!

I'LL SUDDENLY SHOW HIM THIS BIG SPIDER I'VE GOT IN MY HAND!
HIC!

HA-HA!

HIC! NO THANKS– I'M NOT HUNGRY.
2651

I'VE GOT THE PERFECT ANSWER FOR YOUR HICCUPS...
HIC!
2652

...CLOSE YOUR EYES, HOLD YOUR BREATH AND COUNT TO 100.
HIC!

ONE... HIC... TWO... THREE... FOUR.. HIC!
IT DOESN'T ACTUALLY HELP BUT I ENJOY IT!

ER... HELLO, SARGE!
WHAT ARE YOU DOING, PEEP?
2653

I'M GOING TO GIVE MAD PIERRE A FRIGHT TO CURE HIS HICCUPS.

IDIOTS SCARE HIM, DO THEY?

THIS'LL CURE HIS HICCUPS!
HIC!
2654

WHAA!

WHACK!

YOU SCARED HIM ALL RIGHT—HE THOUGHT HE'D KILLED YOU.

PROMISE ME SOMETHING, DENNIS.
2655
THE COLONEL'S DAUGHTER IS HERE AND—
BE THE MOTHER OF MY CHILD!
—I DON'T WANT YOU GETTING EXCITED.

THE COLONEL'S DAUGHTER IS THE LOVELIEST GIRL IN THE WORLD!

I THOUGHT YOU LOVED VERA OF THE SEVEN VEILS?
NAH...

...I ONLY LOVE *BITS* OF HER.
2656

I'M GOING TO GIVE THE COLONEL'S DAUGHTER A PRESENT.
2657

IS THAT WHAT I THINK IT IS?
MIGHT BE.

DENNIS, YOU CAN'T GIVE THOSE Y FRONTS YOUR MUM SENT YOU.

HELLO.
GRZSPLT!

COULD YOU TELL ME THE TIME?

HE STARTED DRIBBLING THEN HE RIPPED OFF HIS WATCH AND GAVE IT TO ME.
2658

YOU HAVE TO FORGIVE MY FRIEND DENNIS.
2659

YOU SEE, HE FINDS YOU VERY ATTRACTIVE BUT HE'S NOT A SCHOLAR.

HE HAS DIFFICULTY EXPRESSING HIS ADMIRATION.
SPLUNGE!

SNIFF! THE COLONEL'S DAUGHTER HAS LEFT.
2660

AT LEAST, I HAVE A LOCK OF HER HAIR TO REMEMBER HER BY.

THAT'S NICE WHEN DID SHE GIVE YOU THAT?

SHE DIDN'T—I MANAGED TO GRAB SOME AS SHE WENT THROUGH THE GATE.

OKAY, EGON— WHAT IS IT?
MINCE SURPRISE.
2661

ACTUALLY, IT SMELLS QUITE NICE.

I KNOW— SURPRISED THE HELL OUT OF ME, TOO.

I'VE COME UP WITH A NEW "FUN MENU."
2662

SELECT ONE DISH FROM COLUMN "A" AND ONE FROM COLUMN "B"

BUT IT'S ONLY GOT MINCE UNDER BOTH COLUMNS.

FUN, ISN'T IT?

NOT MINCE AGAIN?
YEP.
2663

I HOPE THERE'S NO GRISTLE IN IT.
NONE AT ALL.

IS IT FINELY CHOPPED?

I'M NOT ONE TO BOAST BUT IT'S BRILLIANTLY CHOPPED!

MINCE, MINCE, GLORIOUS MINCE!
2664

IF I GO WITHOUT IT, IT SURE MAKES ME WINCE!

SIGH!
I DON'T KNOW WHAT IT IS ABOUT THIS STUFF BUT IT REALLY BRINGS OUT THE POET IN ME!

GLOOP!

GUESS WHAT'S FOR DINNER?
MINCE!

THAT HORRIBLE, BROWN, WATERY SLOP YOU'VE BEEN SERVING ALL WEEK!

CLOSE...

BUT IT'S ACTUALLY BLACK NOW—I BURNED IT THIS MORNING.
2665

DINNER COMING UP!
IF HE SERVES MINCE AGAIN, I WON'T BE RESPONSIBLE FOR MY ACTIONS!

HERE WE ARE, A NICE PLATE OF MI—
KLANG!

A NICE PLATE OF MIXED SALAD. THERE'S A RADISH UP MY NOSE.
2666

THERE LIES THE CAMP OF MY PEOPLE.

I WONDER IF THEY'VE FORGOTTEN MY BANISHMENT?

WHEEEEE
BOOM!

NO.
2667

MY BANISHMENT FROM THIS TRIBE WAS THE BEST THING THAT COULD HAVE HAPPENED TO ME!

I'M NOW RICH AND FAMOUS WITH 2000 WIVES!

STILL A LIAR, EH?
YEP—HE'S STILL UGLY, TOO.
2668

HERE COMES THE LEADER OF MY TRIBE—I'LL ACT HUMBLE!

I HAVE RETURNED, OH GRACIOUS ONE, TO BEG FORGIVENESS!

THIS IS BOUND TO IMPRESS HIM!

I CAN SEE MY TENT FROM HERE!
2669

SURELY YOU KNOW THE TERMS OF YOUR BANISHMENT BY NOW?

IT WILL END ONLY WHEN YOU BRING THE HEAD OF AN ENEMY SOLDIER.

WHAT?
YOU DIDN'T GET THEM?

THE HEADS? DAMN THAT POST OFFICE– I'VE SENT HUNDREDS!
2670

GO FROM THIS CAMP NOW!

YOU ARE A THIEF, A LIAR AND A CHEAT!

YOU ARE WITHOUT COURAGE AND WITHOUT HONOUR.

WELL, IS IT OKAY IF I PICK UP MY WHOOPEE CUSHION?
2671

RIGHT–THIS IS YOUR LAST CHANCE!

I'LL COUNT TO TEN AND IF YOU DON'T ASK ME BACK INTO THE TRIBE, I'M OFF FOREVER!

...NINE AND TWENTY THREE THOUSANDTHS... NINE AND TWENTY FOUR...
2672

BOY, WAS I LUCKY!
NOT THE PET SHOP AGAIN.
2673

YEP! A REAL BARGAIN—I BOUGHT A MAN-EATING SHARK!

YOU BOUGHT A HALIBUT.

IT'S NOT A SHARK, THEN?
IT'S A HALIBUT.
2674

BUT THE MAN IN THE PET SHOP SAID TO BE CAREFUL OR IT WOULD HAVE MY ARM OFF.

PERHAPS IT'S GOT A CHAINSAW.

I STILL SAY IT'S A SHARK!
IT'S A HALIBUT!
2675

DENNIS, SHARKS ARE 10 FEET LONG AND CAN BITE YOUR LEG OFF!

IT WOULD TAKE THAT THING 6 MONTHS TO GET THROUGH YOUR SOCK!

YOU SAY THAT FISH IS A HALIBUT AND I SAY IT'S A SHARK?
YES.
RIGHT-PUT YOUR HAND IN THE BUCKET!
WHAT?
IF IT'S A HALIBUT YOU'VE NOTHING TO WORRY ABOUT!
OKAY!
HANG ON-WHAT IF HALIBUTS NIBBLE OR SOMETHING?
2676

RIGHT, WHAT'S GOING ON?
WELL, DENNIS BOUGHT THIS FISH AT THE PET SHOP AN' HE SAYS IT'S A SHARK AND I SAY IT'S A HALIBUT...
...SO I'M PUTTING MY HAND IN TO PROVE IT'S.... IT'S... IT'S...
...I SUPPOSE YOU THINK WE SHOULDN'T BE HALIBUT TESTING ON DUTY?
2677

POOR DENNIS—THE SERGEANT CONFISCATED HIS PET HALIBUT.

YOU WOULDN'T BELIEVE A MAN COULD GET ATTACHED TO SUCH A SIMPLE CREATURE.

BUT, DAMMIT, I REALLY LIKE THE LITTLE CHAP!
2678

IT'S NOT LIKE DENNIS TO BE LATE FOR DUTY.

WHERE ON EARTH COULD HE HAVE BEEN?

KLUNK!

TWO GUESHES!
2679

DENNIS, LOOK AT THE STATE OF YOU!
2680

WHERE HAVE YOU BEEN? WHERE ARE YOUR CLOTHES?

QUESTIONS, QUESTIONS! I'LL GIVE *YOU* A QUESTION!

WHERE ARE YOU?

HOW ON EARTH DID YOU GET INTO THIS STATE?
2681

YOU MEAN YOU DON'T KNOW?
NO.

IT'S REALLY EASY— YOU JUST DRINK LOTS!

DENNIS, WE'VE GOT TO HIDE YOU!
WHY?
2683

BECAUSE YOU'RE BLOTTO AND IT'LL BE THE SERGEANT'S ROUND ANY MINUTE!

I'M NOT MISSING THAT! A PINT OF BEST SARGE!

OH, NO - IT'S THE SERGEANT! GET DOWN BEHIND ME!
2683

WHERE'S PRATT?
ER... CHECKING THE GATE, SARGE!

PHEW! I THINK WE'VE GOT AWAY WITH IT!

HERE, WHAT A BIG BOTTOM YOU'VE GOT, BEAU!

POOR DENNIS- CAUGHT BEING DRUNK ON DUTY!
2684

IN THE OLD DAYS A MAN WOULD GET SHOT FOR THAT KIND OF THING.

IT'S NOT A HELL OF A LOT OF FUN THESE DAYS EITHER.

SHPLUT!
2685
MY BLADE AWAITS YOUR DYING RAYS, OH SUN GOD!
HERE I WILL STAND UNTIL YOUR FINAL BEAM REFLECTS FROM THAT BLOOD-SOAKED STEEL TO A SACRED SPOT.
THEN IT'S KIPPY-BYES FOR THE NIGHT.

AH, THAT WAS A GOOD SLEEP!
STRETCH!

A NEW ENERGY IS COURSING THROUGH MY VEINS...

...I FEEL COMPLETELY REFRESHED AND READY TO FACE THE WORLD!

ZZZZZZ
2686

I SEEM TO GET LAZIER EVERY DAY.

I KNOW—I'LL TOSS A COIN TO SEE WHAT I SHOULD DO TODAY.

HEADS, IT'S FORTY WINKS—TAILS, IT'S A PROPER SLEEP.
2687

LET'S SEE NOW – I'VE HAD A GOOD NIGHT'S SLEEP...

FOLLOWED BY FORTY WINKS AND AN AFTER-LUNCH KIP.

I'M GOING TO BE HARD PUSHED TO FIT IN MY AFTERNOON SIESTA.
2688

MORNING, FOUR EYES– IT LOOKS PRETTY FOUL TODAY.
2689

OH, I DON'T KNOW– I'M SURE THE SUN WILL BREAK THROUGH.

I WAS TALKING ABOUT YOUR FACE.

YOU'RE THE LAZIEST PERSON I'VE EVER SEEN IN MY LIFE!
2690

YOU CAN'T TALK TO ME LIKE THAT!

PUNCH YOURSELF IN THE FACE!

YOU KNOW, I OFTEN WISH I'D BEEN A WRITER.
2691

ONE SHOULD NEVER UNDERESTIMATE THE POWER OF THE PEN.

YOU'RE TELLING ME– I GOT ONE STUCK UP MY NOSE ONCE.

WHAT ARE YOU DOING, BEAU?
WRITING A PLAY.
2692

IT'S ABOUT ROME AND THE END OF THE EMPIRE.

WHAT, A PLAY ABOUT A PICTURE-HOUSE CLOSING DOWN?

IT'S NOT EASY BEING A WRITER, YOU KNOW.
2693

I CAN SPEND HOURS JUST GROPING FOR A SINGLE WORD!

NO, DENNIS, I DID **NOT** SAY I WAS GROPING A SINGLE BIRD.

The forest was dark and the fog was...
2694

...extremely thick.

HOW'S THE PLAY GOING?
TERRIBLE.
2695

I'M HAVING TROUBLE WITH THE MOTIVATION OF THE MAIN CHARACTER.

LATTERLY HE FEELS PARANOIAC ABOUT THE FUTILITY OF MAN'S EXISTENCE BUT—
IS THERE ANY SNOGGING IN IT?

MY PLAY IS FINISHED!
2696

IS THE WORLD READY FOR A NEW LITERARY GENIUS...

...A MASTER WORDSMITH WHOSE GRASP OF VOCABULARY IS SECOND TO NONE?

WHAT'S THE TITLE?
I COULDN'T THINK OF ONE.

DENNIS HAS ASKED ME TO MEET HIM IN THE PUB.

GOOD OLD DENNIS —I THOUGHT HE'D FORGOTTEN MY BIRTHDAY!
BAR

HE'S PROBABLY ORGANISED A SURPRISE PARTY.

ABOUT TIME— LEND US A QUID!
2697

IT'S TRUE—HE *HAS* FORGOTTEN MY BIRTHDAY.
2699

WELL, I'M CERTAINLY NOT GOING TO REMIND HIM.

I SIMPLY WON'T MENTION THE SUBJECT.

HAVE YOU SEEN MY CANDLES?

DO YOU KNOW WHAT DAY IT IS TODAY?
NO.
2700

A SPECIAL DAY FOR ME. PEOPLE SING ME A SONG—ONE THAT STARTS WITH "*HAPPY.*"

HAPPY DAYS ARE HERE AGAIN

RIGHT, DENNIS—
NO MORE SUBTLE
HINTING!
2701

HAPPY BIRTHDAY
TO ME! HAPPY
BIRTHDAY TO ME!

NOW, WHAT DOES
THAT SUGGEST
TO YOU?

YOU CAN'T
SING.

I'VE TRIED TO
TELL YOU THIS
IS MY SPECIAL
DAY.

I'VE TALKED
ABOUT CANDLES,
CAKES AND
PRESENTS...

...I'VE EVEN
SUNG "HAPPY
BIRTHDAY" TO
MYSELF!

HERE, THAT
REMINDS ME—
WHEN'S YOUR
BIRTHDAY?
2702

FANCY A GAME OF BASKETBALL, PEEP?

NO THANKS, PIERRE— I'M WRITING A LETTER.

DO YOU WANT TO FINISH IT FROM A HOSPITAL BED?
2313

LET'S SHOOT BASKETS, BIG BOY!

I'M NOT SURE OF THE RULES OF BASKETBALL.
2314

YOU TRY TO TAKE THE BALL FROM ME AND I PUNCH YOU.

IS THERE OFFSIDE?
YES—YOU GET PUNCHED FOR THAT.

SEEMS STRAIGHTFORWARD.
NO TALKING— PUNCHING OFFENCE.

TRY AND TAKE THE BALL OFF ME, PIERRE.

REMEMBER— BASKETBALL IS A NON-CONTACT SPORT!

WHACK!

I DIDN'T CONTACT YOU TO TELL YOU I WAS GOING TO PUNCH YOU.
2315

PIERRE, BASKETBALL IS A NON-CONTACT SPORT.
THAT MEANS YOU'RE NOT ALLOWED TO TOUCH ME.
BOING!
2316

LET'S GO THROUGH THIS FROM THE START.

THAT'S ANOTHER GOAL TO ME.
BASKET.
2317

WHACK!
YOU MISUNDERSTAND. I WASN'T CALLING YOU A—

SHALL WE STOP NOW? I'LL NEVER PULL BACK 12 GOALS.

I'VE JUST BEEN PLAYING BASKETBALL WITH YOUR MATE.
2318

IT WAS GREAT FUN!

YES, YOU SHOULD HAVE BEEN HERE.

OH, NO—I HOPE DENNIS DOESN'T HEAR ABOUT THIS.
TONIGHT
VERA OF THE SEVEN VEILS
2325

THANKFULLY, HE CAN'T READ, AND WITH LUCK, NOBODY WILL MENTION IT.
TONIGHT
VERA OF THE SEVEN VEILS

SHE'S IN TOWN—I CAN SMELL HER!
TONIGHT
VERA OF THE SEVEN VEILS

BEFORE WE GO IN, HERE ARE THE RULES...
BAR
TONIGHT
VERA OF THE SEVEN VEILS
2514

NO SHOUTING, WHISTLING OR JUMPING ON THE STAGE.

IN FACT YOU'RE NOT TO TRY AND CATCH HER ATTENTION IN ANY WAY.

WHAT ABOUT THIS RO—
NO.

IT'S A LOVELY NAME, ISN'T IT?
TONIGHT
VERA OF THE SEVEN VEILS

SORT OF ROLLS OFF YOUR TONGUE.
TONIGHT
VERA OF THE SEVEN VEILS

TONIGHT
VERA OF THE SEVEN VEILS
2515

YES, I LIKE BEING CALLED DENNIS.
TONIGHT
VERA OF THE SEVEN VEILS

HERE SHE COMES NOW, DENNIS.
TONIGHT
VERA OF THE SEVEN VEILS
2516
REMEMBER, NO—
VERA! YOU PRINCESS OF BEAUTY YOU!
LOVER BOY'S HERE! I WORSHIP THE EARTH YOU WALK ON!
GOOD IDEA, DENNIS—PLAY HARD TO GET.

SHE *IS* GOOD— I'LL GIVE YOU THAT.
TONIGHT
VERA OF THE SEVEN VEILS
2517
IT'S REALLY QUITE ARTFUL— THE TANTALISING BUILD-UP THE SUBTLETY OF MOVEMENT...

...AN ALMOST HYPNOTIC—
GET 'EM OFF— WE'RE GROWING OLD OUT HERE!

THROWN OUT AGAIN—ALL BECAUSE OF YOUR JUVENILE MIND!
2518

I'M SURE YOU COULD FIND SOMETHING SMUTTY IN "SNOW WHITE."

IS THAT THE ONE ABOUT THE BLONDE WHO'S KIPPED UP WITH SEVEN BLOKES?

WHAT I'D GIVE FOR A DEAD GOAT!

THERE JUST DOESN'T SEEM TO BE THE SAME AMOUNT OF DEAD ANIMALS AROUND AS THERE USED TO BE.

HELLO, LITTLE BIRDIE!
EXCEPTING THOSE FROM THE NECK UP.
2519

I WISH YOU COULD TEACH ME TO FLY!

IT WOULD BE GREAT TO SOAR AROUND THE SKY LIKE WHAT YOU DO!

I SEE YOUR GRAMMAR MATCHES YOUR LOOKS.
2520

LOOK WHAT I'VE BROUGHT YOU...

...IT'S A LITTLE BELL FOR YOU TO PLAY WITH!
A BELL?

OH, I SEE—ROOM SERVICE! ONE DEAD GOAT, PLEASE!
DING!
2521

DO YOU LIKE YOUR LITTLE BELL?
SUPER.

YOU CAN PLAY WITH THAT FOR HOURS.
WHOOPEE.

DING.
2522

I DOUBT IF I'LL SLEEP TONIGHT—I'LL BE SICK WITH EXCITEMENT.

HELLO AGAIN LITTLE BIRDIE!

YOU'RE GLAD TO SEE ME AREN'T YOU? I CAN READ YOUR MIND.

THEN YOU'LL ALSO KNOW THAT ONE MORE STEP AND I'M HAVING YOUR NOSE.
2523

DO YOU SEE THAT VULTURE OUT THERE?
YES.

HE'S VERY TAME. IT'S FUNNY BUT I CAN TELL HE SORT OF RESPECTS ME.

HELLO—I SEE "HADDOCK-BRAIN" IS BACK AT WORK.
2524

IT'S BRILLIANT! FIRST I GET DELIVERED INSIDE THE FORT...
MERRY XMAS TO BEAU PEEP
2525

...THEN, AT NIGHT, I BREAK OUT AND WISH BEAU PEEP A MERRY CHRISTMAS...
MERRY XMAS TO BEAU PEEP

...WITH A BASEBALL BAT WHILE HE'S ASLEEP!
MERRY XMAS TO BEAU PEEP

YOU'VE GOT TO BE CUNNING TO SURVIVE IN MY BUSINESS!
MERRY XMAS TO BEAU PEEP
2526

WHO WOULD GUESS THAT THIS INNOCENT PACKAGE CONTAINS A BLOODTHIRSTY ASSASSIN?
MERRY XMAS TO BEAU PEEP

...WHO NEARLY BECAME A SOPRANO BY SITTING ON HIS SWORD.
MERRY XMAS TO BEAU PEEP

I CAN'T WAIT TO SEE PEEP'S FACE WHEN HE OPENS THIS PARCEL!
MERRY XMAS TO BEAU PEEP

I CAN SAFELY SAY IT'S GOING TO BE THE BIGGEST CHRISTMAS SURPRISE *HE'S* EVER HAD...
MERRY XMAS TO BEAU PEEP

...A BASEBALL-BAT-IN-THE-MOUTH-O-GRAM!
MERRY XMAS TO BEAU PEEP
2527

SOMEONE'S COMING! MY HOURS OF WAITING ARE OVER!
MERRY XMAS TO BEAU PEEP
2528

NOTHING CAN GO WRONG NOW! A PLAN OF MINE IS ACTUALLY GOING TO WORK!
MERRY XMAS TO BEAU PEEP

OH, NO-QUICK! RUB MY LEG! RUB MY LEG! I'VE GOT CRAMP!

I MUST ADMIT YOUR PLAN NEARLY WORKED.
MERRY XMAS TO BEAU PEEP
2529

QUITE CLEVER THAT— HIDING INSIDE A FAKE CHRISTMAS PARCEL.

WHAT GAVE YOU THE IDEA?
I COULDN'T FIT IN THE TURKEY.

SIGH. FAILED AGAIN.
2530

AT LEAST I HAVE FAILED IN A MANNER BEFITTING MY PEOPLE— WITH DIGNITY.

JUST ONCE! LET ME WIN JUST ONCE!

YEAR IN, YEAR OUT YOU'VE STOOD ON THIS WALL, PEEP...
2531

...BRAVELY DEFENDING US AGAINST ALL SORTS OF DANGER.

YOU'RE IN LINE FOR A DECORATION, SOLDIER!
I AM?

THANK YOU VERY MUCH, SIR.

HERE'S YOUR PRESENT, BEAU.
A DOMINO.
2532

YOU GAVE ME A DOMINO LAST YEAR.
I KNOW! AND LOOK— IT'S JUST THE SAME...

...I THOUGHT YOU MIGHT LIKE TO COLLECT DOUBLE-FOURS!

DO YOU LIKE THE WATCH I GAVE YOU, DENNIS?
YEAH.
2534

I HAD YOUR NAME INSCRIBED ON THE BACK.
I NOTICED...

...IT'S JUST THAT IT MAKES IT HARDER TO FLOG.

SIGH! THE END OF ANOTHER YEAR...
DIARY
2535

...AND WHAT AN EXCITING YEAR IT WAS! JUST LOOK AT MY DIARY!
DIARY

"MARCH 8TH. FOUND A PIECE OF WOOL."
DIARY

THIS IS SO DEPRESSING.
DIARY
2536

I WAS GOING TO HAVE MY DIARY PUBLISHED...
DIARY

...A CATALOGUE OF ADVENTURE, PASSION AND COURAGE.
DIARY

"APRIL 24TH. OFF SICK WITH THE TUMMY TROTS."
DIARY

THIS IS MY RESOLUTION, DENNIS.
2540

"THIS YEAR I VOW TO MAKE A SERGEANT."

WHAT, WITH PLASTICINE?

A TOAST, DENNIS!

MAY THIS BE THE YEAR THAT ALL YOUR DREAMS COME TRUE!

HANG ON...
SIP!

...LAST NIGHT I DREAMED I WAS A BADGER.
2541

EVERY NEW YEAR I THINK THE SAME THINGS.
2542

WHAT HAVE I ACHIEVED? WHAT *WILL* I ACHIEVE?

IT'S SO IMPORTANT TO **KNOW** WHERE YOU'RE GOING!

THE TOILET.

I ENVY YOU, DENNIS.
2543

YOU'RE HAPPY WITH YOUR LOT IN LIFE.

DON'T YOU EVER WANT ANYTHING MORE?

OH, ALL RIGHT—I'LL HAVE ANOTHER WINE.

DENNIS HAS JUST REALISED IT'S HIS ROUND.
2544

I WONDER IF IT'LL BE THE LEFT OR RIGHT TODAY?

OOH — I FEEL SO FAINT!
SWOON!

RIGHT.

YOU'RE SO MEAN, DENNIS!
2545

WELL, I'M NOT MOVING TILL YOU BUY A ROUND!

BUY US A DRINK WHILE WE'RE WAITING.

YOU'RE SO MEAN, DENNIS, IT'S UNBELIEVABLE!
BAR
2546

THREE HOURS WITHOUT BUYING A ROUND— THAT'S A RECORD!
BA

THAT'S WORTH CELEBRATING— BUY US A PINT!

LET ME WORK THIS OUT— THERE'S NO SIGN OF EGON...
CANTEEN

...AND THIS IS A DELIVERY NOTE FOR 2 CASES OF COOKING SHERRY.

HE WOULDN'T... NOT AGAIN...

AM I SITTING COMFORTABLY ? THEN I'LL BEGIN.
SHERRY
2547

LET'S SEE— HAVE I GOT EVERYTHING ?
SHERRY
2548

2 CASES OF SHERRY, A BALLOON AND MYSELF.
SHERRY

THIS HAS THE MAKINGS OF ONE HELLUVA PARTY !
SHERRY

THIS IS A GREAT PARTY !
SHERRY
2549

MAYBE IT'S TIME FOR A FEW GAMES.
SHERRY

I THINK I'LL START WITH "FIND-THE-LIPS."

TIME FOR ANOTHER PARTY GAME, I THINK.
SHERRY
2550

I KNOW – I'LL PLAY TWENTY QUESTIONS!
SHERRY

IS IT DAVY CROCKETT? CORRECT – HAVE A DRINK!

EGON, WHAT ON EARTH ARE YOU DOING?
HAVING A PARTY.
SHERRY
2551

BY YOURSELF?
DON'T BE STUPID!
SHERRY

I'VE GOT TWO CASES OF SHERRY!
SHERRY

HOW'S EGON?
NOT BAD...
2552

...THOUGH I THINK HE'S A BIT HUNG-OVER AFTER ALL HIS CELEBRATING.

THAT'S HIS EFFORT AT CHIPS.

WELL, HERE THEY ARE — MY LIFE'S POSSESSIONS...
2553

...CARRIED WITH ME ALWAYS AS A REMINDER OF MY ACHIEVEMENTS.

AN ASHTRAY AND THE LITTLE RACING CAR FROM MONOPOLY.

IT'S NOT MUCH, IS IT?
2554

MY LIFE'S POSSESSIONS IN ONE TINY, FADED, LEATHER POUCH.

AND I NICKED THAT FROM A BUS CONDUCTOR.

MY GRANDFATHER GAVE ME THIS BOX ON HIS DEATH-BED.
2555

HE TOLD ME ONLY TO OPEN IT IF I WAS IN TROUBLE.

A WHISTLE.

THIS IS ALL MY GRANDFATHER LEFT ME—A WHISTLE.
2556

WAIT—THERE'S A NOTE INSIDE.

I KNEW IT—IT'S PROBABLY A MAP OF WHEREVER HE BURIED HIS MONEY!

"PLACE IN LIPS AND BLOW."

MAYBE THIS WHISTLE MY GRANDFATHER LEFT ME IS LIKE A KEY!
2557.

MAYBE WHEN I BLOW IT THE PERFECT PITCH WILL VIBRATE SOME ROCKS LOOSE AND THERE WILL BE A FORTUNE HIDDEN UNDERNEATH!

PHHH!

THERE'S NO PEA IN IT.

SO WHAT IF I DON'T HAVE ANY POSSESSIONS!
2558

I'VE GOT LOTS OF OTHER THINGS GOING FOR ME LIKE... LIKE...

...ARMPITS THAT WORK!

SIGH! THAT'S THE ONE THING THAT KEEPS ME GOING...
2295

...THE KNOWLEDGE THAT THE MEN ADMIRE AND RESPECT ME.

WHAT'S OLD LOONEY-DRAWERS DOING AT THE WINDOW?

THAT'S IT—THE PERFECT WAY TO FIND OUT WHAT THE MEN REALLY THINK OF ME!
2296

I'LL DISGUISE MYSELF AND MINGLE AMONGST THEM...

...THEN CASUALLY BRING UP THE SUBJECT!

MORNING! THAT COLONEL'S A FAB BLOKE, EH?

THE COLONEL ACTUALLY BELIEVES I DON'T RECOGNISE HIM!

A FEW SUBTLE COMMENTS COULD HELP MY CAREER HERE.

I LOVE MY COLONEL SO MUCH I CRY MYSELF TO SLEEP EVERY NIGHT!
2297

I WAS JUST THINKING WHAT A WONDERFUL COLONEL WE HAVE...

...WISE, HANDSOME, WITTY, BRAVE— WHAT A MAN!

COLONEL!
LOOK!—IT'S ME!

I'M SO EMBARRASSED I'D HARDLY BE ABLE TO ACCEPT PROMOTION!
2298

ONE EXPRESSION SPRINGS TO MIND WHEN I LOOK AT YOU, PEEP...

..."SERGEANT MATERIAL" —AND YOU HAVE IT!
I DO?

YES—THAT'S THE SAME MATERIAL SERGEANTS WEAR.
2299

I'M NOT GOING TO BE AROUND FOR EVER, PEEP.

WHEN I LOOK AT YOU, I SEE THE MAN WHO WILL ONE DAY BE COLONEL.
YOU DO?

YES—I CAN SEE SERGEANT BIDET REFLECTED IN YOUR EYES.
2300

THIS WILL BE A SPECIAL SURVIVAL COURSE.
2301

YOU WILL EACH BE GIVEN A KNIFE, SOME STRING AND MATCHES. RIGHT— DISMISS!

ER... IT'S PROBABLY JUST ME— BUT I DIDN'T HEAR ANY MENTION OF BEER AND SANDWICHES!

THIS WILL TEST OUR INITIATIVE, DENNIS...
2302

...SURVIVE FOR A WEEK WITH ONLY A KNIFE, STRING AND MATCHES.

OUR VERY LIVES DEPEND ON THESE LITTLE KITS.

I SWAPPED MINE FOR A SQUIRT-RING!

HOW CAN WE POSSIBLY SURVIVE WITH JUST A KNIFE, SOME STRING AND MATCHES?
2303

I KNOW! CUT UP THE STRING WITH THE KNIFE AND LIGHT IT WITH THE MATCHES!
CLICK!

CLOSE YOUR EYES, DENNIS— I'M GOING TO SLAP YOU.

WHAT ARE YOU DOING, BEAU?
2304

I'M USING THIS STRING TO MAKE A SNARE.

SOME ANIMALS ARE REALLY STUPID —THEY WALK RIGHT INTO IT.

I'LL PROBABLY CATCH YOUR MUM.

YOU WOULDN'T THINK IT POSSIBLE, WOULD YOU?
2305
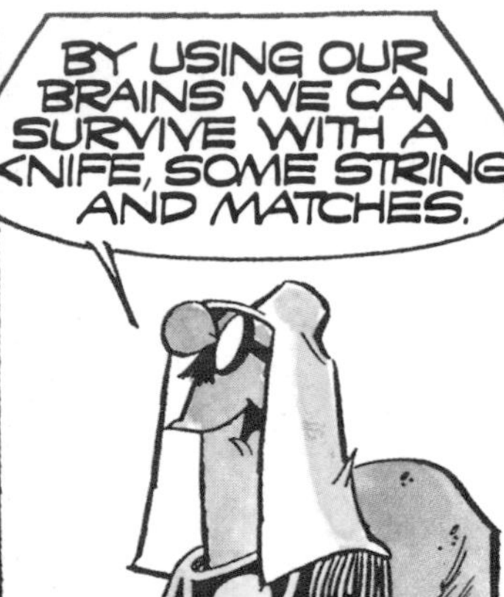
BY USING OUR BRAINS WE CAN SURVIVE WITH A KNIFE, SOME STRING AND MATCHES.

D'YOU WANT SOME MORE STRING?
NO THANKS— I'M FULL.

YOUR SURVIVAL KIT WAS SPECIALLY DESIGNED.

IT HAD EVERYTHING NEEDED TO HUNT AND KILL YOUR OWN FOOD.
2306

AND YOU ATE IT.
JUST TO WASH DOWN OUR UNIFORMS.

ASTRO, THE OLD WISE SOOTHSAYER WILL HELP ME.
ASTRO
2307

HE WILL HELP ME UNDERSTAND WHY MY QUEST FOR SUCCESS HAS SO FAR BEEN FRUITLESS.

BECAUSE YOU'RE STUPID.

YOU'RE TELLING ME I'M NOT SUCCESSFUL BECAUSE I'M STUPID?
YES.

THERE MUST BE MORE TO IT THAN THAT!
2308

HAVE YOU CONSULTED THE STARS? MAYBE I WAS BORN UNLUCKY?

NO. JUST STUPID.

MAYBE WE SHOULD EXPLORE THE REASONS FOR YOUR FAILURE IN LIFE.

YOU'RE STUPID, TINY, PODGY, UGLY AND OBNOXIOUS.

2309

THAT'S ONE HAND FILLED UP AND I'VE JUST STARTED.

MAYBE THE REASON FOR YOUR FAILURES IS HEREDITARY.

WHAT DID YOUR FATHER DO?

HE OWNED THE SAHARA WATER-SKI CLUB.
2310

SOMETIMES YOUR LIFE CAN BE SHAPED BY YOUR MOTHER.

PERHAPS AN INCIDENT WHILE SHE WAS PREGNANT WITH YOU...

...THAT COULD DETERMINE YOUR PERSONALITY.

WAS SHE FRIGHTENED BY TWO SHORT PLANKS?
2311

I'LL PROVE I'M NOT A FAILURE!

THE NEXT TIME I VISIT THIS TENT I'LL BE A SUCCESS!

WHY ARE YOU STANDING IN MY COAT?
2312

OASIS, OASIS ON THE GROUND...
2319

...WHO IS THE FAIREST ONE AROUND?

YOU ARE, OH HANDSOME ONE!

YOU'RE ALSO GOING DAFT!

ROLL UP! ROLL UP!
THE MAGIC OASIS
2320

THESE MYSTICAL WATERS ACTUALLY SPEAK!
THE MAGIC OASIS

WE CAN SING AS WELL.
THE MAGIC OASIS

MUSICAL REQUESTS A SPECIALITY!

YOU'RE A VERY LUCKY MAN, SIR!
THE MAGIC OASIS
2321

FOR A SMALL SUM, THIS OASIS WILL TALK TO YOU.
THE MAGIC OASIS

THAT'S INCREDIBLE— WHERE'S MY WALLET?

I WANT TO STUFF IT IN MY MOUTH TO STOP ME LAUGHING.

HONESTLY, THESE WATERS ACTUALLY TALK!
THE MAGIC OASIS
2322

GREETINGS, OH HANDSOME STRANGER!

DID YOU HEAR THAT? THAT'S MAGIC, THAT IS!

IT CERTAINLY IS — HOW SO MUCH STUPIDITY GETS INTO ONE HEAD.

THAT OASIS DOESN'T TALK— YOU DO!
THE MAGIC OASIS
2323

LET'S HEAR IT SPEAK WHEN YOU DON'T HAVE YOUR HAND OVER YOUR MOUTH.

HMM...HMM... HMMMIE...HMM...

IT WANTS TO HUM YOU A MESSAGE.

IT'S ALL A JOKE — YOU'D DO ANYTHING FOR MONEY!
THE MAGIC OASIS

I WOULD NOT! MONEY MEANS NOTHING TO ME!
THE MAGIC OASIS

THE MAGIC OASIS

HOW MUCH WILL YOU GIVE ME FOR AN EXCLUSIVE CONFESSION THAT IT'S A FAKE?
THE MAGIC OASIS
2324